one&one

# Just Looking

Exploring together the life and message of Jesus

24 sessions in the Gospel of Luke

## Andrew Cornes

For all those with whom I have enjoyed Bible-reading partnerships down the years and who have helped me to understand, apply and delight in the Bible's teaching.

One2One Just Looking
© The Good Book Company/Andrew Cornes 2011

The Good Book Company
Elm House, 37 Elm Road
New Malden, Surrey KT3 3HB
Tel (UK): 0345 225 0880
Tel (int): +(44) 208 942 0880
email: admin@thegoodbook.co.uk

thegoodbook
COMPANY

Websites:
UK & Europe: www.thegoodbook.co.uk
N America: www.thegoodbook.com
Australia: www.thegoodbook.com.au
New Zealand: www.thegoodbook.co.nz

ISBN: 9781907377983

Printed in China

Just Looking at Jesus?

> Jesus said: "If anyone's will is to do God's will, he will
> know whether the teaching is from God or whether I am
> speaking on my own authority." JOHN 7 v 17

Jesus has always provoked questions. He did in his own day. He still does today.

People in his day wondered how his teaching could be so penetrating, where he got his miraculous powers from, what his popular appeal was, why he seemed so intent on moving towards his own death, and how he could be so sure that he would, in his own words, "on the third day rise again".

People today often have similar questions. It's important to know whether Jesus really is God's Son, or whether he was just a great and influential religious teacher. If he is, as he claimed, the Son of God, then his teaching is God's teaching... his miracles make sense because they are God at work... his death has great significance for the whole of humankind... and death does not have the last word, because as God's Son he has conquered it.

As the quotation above, from John's account of Jesus' life, shows, Jesus says we can know the answers to these questions. All that is required is honesty (or, as Jesus puts it, to have the "will to do God's will"); to want to know the truth and be willing to act on that truth, wherever the results of our search lead us.

Jesus always welcomed questions, provided people wanted to know the answers. He had little time for those who asked questions but whose minds were closed (and he met many of them), or those who wanted to ask question after question but never came to a conclusion.

This book is for people who have questions and want to know, and then act on, the answers; who begin by "Just Looking", but are willing to come to conclusions and then take action based on what they've discovered.

1. **BIBLE-READING PARTNERSHIP:** This book operates on the principle that "two minds are better than one". It is designed for two people, working through the sessions together. Both of you will have questions; each will have insights into what the passage you are studying is saying; both will find answers as you look at the Bible together. You may both be Christians: or maybe one of you is, and the other is just looking; or perhaps neither of you are. That's fine!

2. **FOCUS ON JESUS:** Jesus is at the heart of the Christian faith. Questions about him are central to Christianity. That is why this book concentrates entirely on one of the accounts of the life of Jesus, the Gospel of Luke.

3. **QUICK, SLOW, FULL, YOUR CHOICE:** 24 sessions will be fine for some who use this book; they will provide a thorough study of the life, teaching, death and resurrection of Jesus. For some, however, 24 sessions will be too many. We therefore suggest four different "routes" through the material in this book:
   *Quick Route:* Five sessions, covering the bare essentials.
   *Slower Route:* Ten sessions, going into some more detail.
   *Full Route:* All 24 sessions.
   *Choice Route:* Each session focuses on a question people often have, and which that particular Bible section answers. So, as you look at the questions on the Contents page, you might like to add sessions to either the Quick or Slower Routes. But we'd suggest you build these on top of one of those two routes, otherwise you may miss out some particularly crucial passages in Luke's Gospel.
   To see the Routes in detail, have a look at the Contents on page 7.

4. **PARTNER:** Choose your Bible-reading partner carefully. If you are married or have a partner, you may want to have that person as your Bible-reading partner. Otherwise we strongly advise that you choose someone of your own sex. It is important that neither of you feels you have all the answers already (or thinks that your partner does!): you're looking for answers from the Bible together.

5. **ONLINE GUIDE:** All you need to answer each question is a Bible and your mind! But if you do just want to check, or there's something that's confusing you, there is an online guide to go with these sessions. If one or both of you are preparing for the session before

meeting, or if you want to use it to clarify something afterwards, we hope you find it useful. Go to: www.thegoodbook.co.uk/just-looking.

6. **FREQUENCY:** The ideal is to meet weekly. Some find it better to meet fortnightly, but meeting up any less regularly than that doesn't really work—it's hard to remember where you've got to!

7. **TIMING:** We suggest that you set aside between an hour and an hour and a quarter, and keep strictly to whatever timing you have agreed. It is normally a good idea to begin the Bible Study as soon as possible after arrival, and to catch up on news at the end rather than the beginning; experience shows that otherwise the time of Bible Study gets squeezed out.
   At the end of each session there is a section entitled "Next Time". In this you are encouraged to read those parts of Luke's Gospel which you would otherwise miss out, and to come to your next meeting ready to mention what has struck you.
   You will soon discover whether you have time to discuss what has struck you from these "missed-out" sections. We suggest you restrict yourself to no more than 5-10 minutes for this discussion before beginning the new session. You may find you don't have time for this at all. Whatever you decide, make sure you have enough unhurried time for talking through the questions in the new session.

8. **STUDYING THE BIBLE:** In each session there is a passage from Luke's Gospel, and questions on it. The aim of these questions is the same as in all genuine study of the Bible: to help us understand what the Bible is saying, and work out how it applies to our life today. Some of the questions are about Luke (the author), or Jesus and the people who originally heard or saw Jesus; and some of the questions are about us and our experience of life and of Jesus Christ today. We suggest you discuss each question as fully as you want, but that you don't get bogged down for too long on any one question. If you don't always have time to discuss every question, that's fine: but make sure you always discuss some of the questions which make you think about the relevance of Jesus and his message to your life today.

9. **PREPARATION:** Some people like to study the passage before they meet and note down their answers in the space provided. Often this makes the discussion more fruitful. But it's not compulsory!

10. **TRANSLATION OF THE BIBLE:** The questions occasionally quote from the ESV (English Standard Version) of the Bible. But it's perfectly possible to answer the questions using any other good modern translation, such as the NIV (New International Version). If you do not have a Bible, we suggest you buy one, perhaps using the same translation as your Bible-reading partner.

11. **PRAYING:** As the quotation at the beginning of this Introduction shows, Jesus said that his teaching was from God. If so, it seems wise to speak to God and ask for his help before you study God's message together.
    You might like to pray this prayer each time before you read the passage and discuss it with each other:
    *Heavenly Father, thank you for Jesus, his life and his teaching. Help us to listen to you and understand him more as we study this passage, and to find our questions being answered. Amen.*
    Some Bible-reading partners like to say a prayer after the study, thanking God for what he has shown them about Jesus.

12. **IF IT DOESN'T WORK OUT:** Sometimes a Bible-reading partnership doesn't really work. Occasionally the partners don't gel, or one partner has to drop out. This is often nobody's fault. We would encourage you to choose a new Bible-reading partner; this new partnership may very likely go well and prove much more helpful.

13. **WHAT NEXT?** At the end of the course there is a page for you to review what you have gained from your discussions together and decide what the next step for each of you will be (page 60).
    You may well want to continue in the same Bible-reading partnership. If so, you could use the further material produced by the Good Book Company:
    • One2One Book One (24 studies in the Gospel of John chapters 13 – 17, Paul's letter to the Philippians and the Psalms)
    • One2One Book Two (24 studies in the Gospel of Matthew 26 – 28, Paul's first letter to the Thessalonians and Genesis 1 – 12)

# contents

**Is this book reliable?**

**Today's passage: Luke chapter 1, verses 1-4**

These sessions should help you understand Jesus Christ more fully: what he did, what his message was, who he claimed to be, why he died and the impact he has had on the people of his own time and on millions from all nations today.

You'll be studying one of the earliest accounts of his life, death and resurrection: Luke's Gospel. But this will only get you closer to the life and teaching of Christ if Luke is an accurate historian. So, after a brief time of getting to know your Bible-reading partner a bit better, this session explores the crucial question: Is Luke's book sufficiently reliable?

**A  WHERE YOU'RE AT**

Each of us has been through different stages in thinking about Jesus. This starts with our childhood and what we were taught then about God or Jesus. Luke's book is all about Jesus.

Write down a brief account of how your thinking about Jesus has changed down the years; perhaps you have sometimes been closer to him and sometimes further away. Where are you at in your thinking about him now?

Begin your session together by each telling as much of the story as you are comfortable with talking about.

**B  HOW LUKE WROTE HIS BOOK**          **Read verses 1-4**

❶ What different kinds of information did Luke have available for writing his book (v 1-3)?

**2** Why did Luke mention that many others had written the story of Christ's life and teaching, do you think (v 1)?

**3** Who did Luke get much of his information from (v 2)?
Why is this significant?

**4** What does verse 3 tell us about Luke as a historian?

**5** What did he want his book to achieve for Theophilus (and for us) (v 3-4)?

## C SUM UP

**6** What is the main thing you've learned from this session?
How does this affect the way you'll read the rest of Luke's book?

## D NEXT TIME...

...you'll be looking at Luke 2 v 8-20.
Before next time, read through Luke 1 v 5 – 2 v 7. Come ready to mention anything that particularly struck you.

*Angels to prayer*     *Luke 1 v 13*
*The Song of Angels*
*No mention of Joseph*

# Session 2 · What was happening at Christmas?

If you're starting with Session 2, it would be good to read before your time together chapter 1 verse 1 to chapter 2 verse 7: the introduction to Luke's book.

**Today's passage: Luke 2 v 8-20**

Now Luke comes to Christmas. It's the best known story of the Christian faith—or is it?! Much of what you read in Luke's Gospel may be new to you, but one of the aims of these sessions is to help you look at what is familiar, and discover meaning in it you'd never seen before. As Luke explains what was happening at the first Christmas, he wants us to think what Jesus Christ means to us, his readers.

## A  WHERE YOU'RE AT

If this is your first session together, look back at the section called "Where you're at" in Session 1 (on page 8). Work through that before continuing with Session 2.

## B  THE ANGEL'S MESSAGE     Read verses 8-12

❶ What, according to the angel, is the central message of Christmas (v10-12)?
Is that what you, and your family, concentrate on at Christmas? Why/why not?

❷ Jesus is called three things in verse 11:
- Saviour—which means Rescuer, from the guilt of our sin
- Christ—which means King: the King who God had promised centuries before
- Lord—which can mean either Master or God.
All are important; but which strikes you the most—and why?

**3** What is the most appropriate way to respond to Jesus' coming (v 9-10)?

---

**C  THE ANGEL CHOIR'S PRAISE**        Read verses 13-14

**4** How does the angel choir respond to the birth of Jesus (v 13-14)? What do they especially mention as a reason to rejoice (v 14)?

---

**D  THE SHEPHERDS' RESPONSE**        Read verses 15-20

**5** In what different ways do the shepherds respond to what they hear and then see (v 15-20)?

**6** What do the shepherds show us about ways we can respond to Jesus coming to this earth (v 15-20)?

---

**E  SUM UP**

**7** What is the main thing that has struck you in this session?

---

**F  NEXT TIME...**

Quick Route: you'll be looking at 8 v 4-15 (p 22). Slower Route: 7 v 36-50 (p 20). Full Route: Luke 3 v 1-22 (p 12).

Before next time, read up to the start of next session's passage and come ready to mention anything that has struck you.

# What was John the Baptist's message?

**Today's passage:** Luke 3 v 1-22

Luke tells us the exact point in history when John the Baptist began his work (v 1-2). He was sent to "prepare the way" (v 4) for Jesus: many of those who responded to John later came to follow Jesus.

All the Gospels are clear that, if we are fully to understand Jesus, we need first to hear and take on board the message of John the Baptist.

*Note: Repentance (v 3) means turning away from living a self-centred life, and turning towards a life with God in charge.*

## A  MESSAGE TO THE PEOPLE　　　　Read verses 1-14

❶ What does John ask from the people if they were to be baptised (v 3)? What kind of things does this mean in practice (v 10-14)?

❷ What does John say that God was promising to forgive (v 3)? Do 21st-century men and women really need forgiveness of sins? Why/why not?

❸ Is John's message relevant for your life today (v2-3)? Why/why not?

## B  MESSAGE ABOUT JESUS　　　　Read verses 15-18

❹ What contrasts does John make between himself and Jesus (v 15-16)? Why (v 15-16)?

❺ When John says Jesus "will baptise you with the Holy Spirit" (v 16), he means: "Jesus will immerse you in, or surround you with, the Holy Spirit". Do you know anyone who is obviously full of the Holy Spirit?

**6** Farmers separate "wheat" (valuable, to be kept) from "chaff" (to be burned) (v17). What does John tell us to do, to make sure that Jesus treats us as "wheat" and not "chaff" (v 3, 17)?

---

**C** **OPPOSITION TO JOHN**                    Read verses 19-20

**7** Why is Herod opposed to John?

**8** Does the message of John (and Jesus) meet opposition in our society today? If so, in what ways?

---

**D** **JOHN'S BAPTISM OF JESUS**                Read verses 21-22

**9** Unusual things happen at Jesus' baptism. What do they tell us about Jesus?

**10** If Jesus is as God describes him (v 22), and does what John says he does (v 16-17), how should we respond to him?

---

**E** **SUM UP**

**11** What is the main thing you've learned from this session?

---

**F** **NEXT TIME...**

...you'll be looking at Luke 4 v 1-13.
   Before next time, read Luke 3 v 23-38, and come ready to talk about why you think Luke included that whole family tree.

# How was Jesus tempted?

**Today's passage: Luke 4 v 1-13**

At the beginning of his public life Jesus was baptised. He heard this ringing endorsement from God his Father: "You are my beloved Son; with you I am well pleased" (3 v 21-22).

Almost immediately after this, Jesus went through a period of fierce and prolonged temptation (4 v 1-13). So what does the fact that he was tempted, and yet overcame temptation, tell us about him?

## A  JESUS WAS TEMPTED                    Read verses 1-2

❶ Jesus is "tempted by the devil" (v 2). Why might the devil want to tempt Jesus so soon after his baptism?

❷ The Holy Spirit "led" Jesus into a place where he was tempted (v 1-2). Can you think why God might have wanted his Son to go through a period of strong temptation?

## B  THE FIRST TEMPTATION                 Read verses 2-4

❸ Why is Jesus particularly vulnerable to the first temptation (v 2-3)?

❹ What conviction enables Jesus not to give in to this temptation (v 4)?

## C  THE SECOND TEMPTATION               Read verses 5-8

❺ What is Jesus being tempted to do in the next temptation (v 5-7)?

**6** How does he overcome that temptation (v 8)?
What does this show us about Jesus' priorities?

<br>

**D   THE THIRD TEMPTATION**　　　　　**Read verses 9-13**

**7** What is so clever about the devil's third temptation?

**8** How would it be "putting God to the test" if Jesus gives in to this temptation (v 9-12)?

**9** What does verse 13 tell us about Jesus' experiences of temptation?

**E   OUR EXPERIENCE AND CHRIST'S EXPERIENCE**

**10** In what ways are our struggles with temptation similar to Jesus' struggles, and in what ways are they different?

**F   SUM UP**

**11** What is the main thing you've learned from this session?

**12** Luke clearly believes Jesus is "God's beloved Son" (3 v 22). How does it affect your view of Jesus to know that he was tempted, and didn't give in to temptation?

**G   NEXT TIME...**

...it's Luke 5 v 1-11.
Before you next meet, read Luke 4 v 14-44 and come ready to talk about anything that has struck you.

# Is it worth trying again?

**Today's passage:** Luke 5 v 1-11

The Gospels are full of stories about Jesus meeting people: what he said to them, what he did for them, what he asked of them, how they responded and how their lives were changed.

One of the best ways of reading them is to try to get inside the mind and experience of the person who Jesus met and, having done so, to think whether we would react (or whether we have reacted) to Jesus in the same way.

In this story we try to get into the mind of Simon, who is best known by his nickname, Peter (see v 8).

## A BEFORE THE CATCH                    Read verses 1-5

❶ What is the first thing Jesus asks Simon to do (v 1-3)?
Imagine you are Simon on that day: what do you think he sees in Jesus which makes him agree to do what Jesus asks (v 1-3)?

❷ What is the next thing Jesus asks Simon to do (v 4)?

❸ What is Simon's immediate reaction to what Jesus says (v 5)?
What is Simon's next reaction to what Jesus says (v 5)?

## B SAME FOR YOU?

❹ Do you ever feel that Jesus (or God) has asked you to do something and you've felt: "I've tried that before and it hasn't worked"?
Have you felt (or do you feel) it is worth trying again?

## C  AFTER THE CATCH                    Read verses 6-11

**5** What happens when Simon does what Jesus asks of him (v 6-7)?

**6** What is Simon's reaction when he sees the catch (v 8)?
On the surface this has nothing to do with catching fish! Why do you think he says it?

**7** What does Jesus then say to Simon (v 10)?
What does Jesus mean by this, do you think?

**8** What impression does this make on Simon and his friends (v 11)?
Why do you think they do something so radical?

## D  SAME FOR YOU?

**9** We may not need to leave *everything* to follow Jesus (v 11) but we will need to leave *some* things. What might you need to leave to follow Jesus? What in this passage shows it is worth it?

## E  SUM UP

**10** What is the main thing you're taking away from this session?

## F  NEXT TIME...

...you'll be looking at Luke 6 v 27-36.
Before then, read up to the beginning of that passage, and come along ready to mention anything that's particularly struck you.

# How should we treat those who dislike us?

**Today's passage:** Luke 6 v 27-36

Becoming a Christian is *not* making some new resolutions and being determined to do good. It is realising that we've gone seriously wrong (that we are "sick"), coming to Jesus for his forgiveness and putting our life in his hands (read 5 v 27-32).

But living the new life that Jesus gives is demanding. It involves, for example, being generous not only to those who like us, but to those who dislike us. This study will be of most value if you think not of people in general, but of specific people who have not treated you well.

---

**A** WHO AND WHAT? **Read verses 27-31**

❶ For the early Christians, who were their "enemies" who "hated ... cursed ... abused/mistreated" them (v 27-28—and look back at 5 v 12 – 6 v 26)?

❷ Who are (or have been, in the past) the people who have hated or abused you (in your workplace, your family, your neighbourhood)?

❸ In v 27-28, what does Jesus say in we must do for these people? How can you take the first step in doing what Jesus says here?

❹ As we read v 29-30, it's easy to think what these verses *can't* mean (eg: "It can't mean: Let a thief get away with it"). What *can* you do to obey what Jesus is saying here?

**5** What do you wish that these people who mistreat you would do for you (v 31)? So what can you do for them (v 31)?

---

**B** **HOW AND WHY?**                    Read verses 32-36

**6** Here "sinners" means those who have no time for God, or Jesus, in their lives. How does Jesus want us to be different from them (v 32-34)?

**7** Jesus tells us to "lend" to those who dislike and mistreat us (v 34-35). What could you lend to the people who dislike you?

**8** Jesus promises a "great reward" for those who obey this difficult teaching (v 35). What reward do you think he had in mind?

**9** Jesus wants us to move from being "sinners" (those who don't make room for Jesus in their lives, v 32-34) to being "sons (and daughters) of the Most High", who know in our experience God's kindness and his mercy (v 35-36).
Is that a change you've seen in a friend of yours? What's been the evidence of the change?

---

**C** **SUM UP**

**10** What is the main thing you have learned from this session?
What can you do about it this week?

---

**D** **NEXT TIME...**

...you'll be studying Luke 7 v 36-50.
Before then, read 6 v 37 – 7 v 35, noting anything that strikes you.

# Why do people love Jesus?

**Today's passage: Luke 7 v 36-50**

A church I know has as its ambition: "Growing in love for Christ". And that is the heart of Christian experience: knowing we are loved by Jesus Christ, loving him in return, and growing in that love.

Most of us know at least one person, perhaps several, who clearly love Jesus. But how can *you* grow to love him; and why should you? This story of a woman's meeting with Jesus offers some important answers.

## A WHAT SHE DID FOR JESUS      Read verses 36-39

**1** What do we know of the woman's past life (v 36-39)?

**2** What exactly does she do (v 37-38))?
What kind of reaction do you think this is likely to prompt at the dinner party?!

**3** What does the host, Simon the Pharisee, think of the incident (v 39)?

**4** Has anyone reacted negatively to you showing an interest in Jesus? If so, how?

## B JESUS' PARABLE      Read verses 40-47

**5** What is the point of Jesus' parable (v 41-42)?
Why does Jesus tell it to Simon at the dinner party (v 40-47)?

**6** How does Jesus contrast Simon's love for him with the woman's (v 44-46)?

**7** Do you know anyone who loves Jesus a great deal (v 47)? If so, how do they show it?

**C** WHY SHE LOVED JESUS     Read verses 47-50

**8** Why does this woman love Jesus so much (v 47-48)?

**9** Why are the dinner guests offended by what Jesus says (v 49)?

**10** What do Jesus' last words to her mean (v 50)?

**11** Could you love Jesus for the same reason: that he is willing to forgive your sins if you have faith in him (v 47-50)?

**12** The woman expresses her love for Jesus in a particular way (v 44-46). If you already share, or if you came to share, this woman's faith (v 50), how might you express your love for Jesus?

**D** SUM UP

**13** What is the main thing you will take away from this session?

**E** NEXT TIME...

Slower and Full Route: Luke 8 v 4-15 (p 22).
    Before next time, read 8 v 1-3. What does this brief paragraph tell us about Jesus?

# How can I be changed by Jesus' teaching?

**Today's passage: Luke 8 v 4-15**

Jesus told many parables; this is one of the most famous. Parables work on two levels: the "story level" (in this case about seed, sowing, different types of soil) and the "meaning level" (what Jesus was wanting to teach—what the different parts of the story represent).

Often Jesus just told the story of the parable. For those whose ears were blocked (see v 8), the story remained just a parable, without revealing the secrets, or truth, which the story was meant to convey (see v 9-10). But in this parable, Jesus not only tells the story (v 5-8), but also explains its meaning (v 11-15).

## A  THE PARABLE                    Read verses 4-15

❶ The seed (story level) represents "the word of God" (meaning level) (v 5, 11). What does "the word of God" (v 11) mean?
Who does the sower/farmer (v 5) represent?
What does the soil/place where the seed falls represent (v 5-8, 11-15)?

❷ What is the overall message of Jesus' parable?

## B  PATH, ROCK, THORNS

❸ What is the experience of those who hearts are like the path (v 5, 12)?

❹ Why does the devil "come and take away" the message (v 12)?

❺ What is the experience of those who are like the rock (v 6, 13)?

**6** What makes the seed on the rock wither/fall away (v 13)?
What do you think Jesus had in mind when he said that (v 13)?

**7** What is the experience of those who are like thorny soil (v 7, 14)?

**8** Why do you think the things Jesus mentions in verse 14 "choke" the message of Christ?

## C THE GOOD SOIL

**9** What is the experience of those whose hearts are like good soil (v 8, 15)?

**10** What have they done that is different from the other groups (v 15)?

## D WHAT ABOUT US?                    Re-read verses 5-8, 11-15

**11** Which type of soil are you most like at the moment in your response to the message of Christ (v 5-8, 11-15)?

*How do you relate to this parable?*

*Does it encourage*

**12** How in practice can you make sure you "hold fast/retain" the message of Christ (v 8, 15)? *Spend time on your relationship*

*Be intentional. (Piano lesson stuff)*

## E NEXT TIME...

Quick Route: Luke 15 v 11-24 (p 40). Slower and Full Route: Luke 9 v 18-27 (p 24).
Before next time, read to the start of next session's passage.

# What does it cost to follow Jesus?

**Today's passage:** Luke 9 v 18-27

Jesus never pulled any punches. He wanted people to follow him (he sometimes called this "entering the kingdom of God", see 9 v 2, 11)—but he wanted them to do it with their eyes open. Receiving his friendship and forgiveness is free; continuing with him is demanding and will mean self-sacrifice. Yet anything that he *asks of us* (see v 23-26) is nothing compared to what he has already *done for us* (v 22).

## A  WHO IS JESUS?                    Read verses 18-20

**1** In Jesus' day, what did the crowds say about Jesus (v 18-19)?

**2** In our society today, what do most people say about Jesus?

**3** Why is it a much bolder statement for Peter to say: "You are the Christ/Messiah of God" (v 20)?

**4** At this stage of your thinking, who would you say Jesus is? Has your thinking about Jesus changed at all as a result of looking at Luke's Gospel?

## B  WHERE JESUS IS HEADING          Read verses 21-22

**5** "The Son of Man" is a name Jesus used to describe himself. Why do you think Jesus tells his disciples in advance what he will go through (v 22)?
What connection does this have with Peter's statement that Jesus is "the Christ/Messiah of God" (v 20-22)?

Note: Nobody quite knows why Jesus instructed them to tell no one he was the Messiah. But it may well have been because most Jews had a totally mistaken idea of what the Messiah would do: they thought he would defeat and drive out the occupying Romans.

## C WHAT FOLLOWING JESUS IS LIKE     Read verses 23-27

**6** What does Jesus say it will mean to follow him (v 23)?
What might that mean in practice for you?

**7** Why does Jesus say it is a wise decision to follow him (v 24-25)?

**8** What does Jesus mean by "saving your life" and "losing your life/ yourself", do you think (v 24-25)?

**9** In practice, how can we prove to "be ashamed" of Jesus and his message (v 26)?
Have you ever been ashamed of Jesus and his message?

**10** What does Jesus mean when he says that, if we are ashamed of him now, he will be ashamed of us in the future (v 26)?
Why does he warn us about this?

Note: Jesus ends on an encouraging note (v 27). The people who will soon "see the kingdom of God" are probably Peter, James and John. Jesus is almost certainly referring to their experience of seeing Jesus' kingly glory in v 28-36.

## D SUM UP

**11** What is the main thing you're taking away from this session?

## E NEXT TIME...

Slower Route: Luke 11 v 1-4 (p 28). Full Route: Luke 10 v 25-42 (p 26).
Read up to your next passage and note down things which strike you.

# How can I love God and my neighbour?

**Today's passage:** Luke 10 v 25-42

People were always asking Jesus questions. Sometimes they really wanted to know the answers; sometimes their motives were more mixed (v 25, 29, 40). Jesus is always willing to answer any genuine question (though he sometimes challenges us with a question of his own: v 26, 36). But when we've understood his teaching, he always wants us to act on what we now know (v 28, 37, 42).

---

**A  THE MAN'S FIRST QUESTION**     Read verses 25-28

❶ Is the man's first question (about how to "inherit eternal life") an important one (v 25)? Why/why not?
Is this a question you are asking? Why/why not?

❷ Put in your own words the answer Jesus agrees with (v 26-28)?

❸ What, in practice, will it mean for you to love God with all your heart, soul, strength and mind (v 27)?

---

**B  THE MAN'S SECOND QUESTION**     Read verses 29-37

❹ Is the man's second question (about who is the neighbour that I'm to love) an important one (v 29)? Why/why not?
Is it a question you are asking? Why/why not?

**5** The man is obviously in desperate need (v 30). Who are the people you know who are most in need, and what are their needs?

**6** What facts are surprising or shocking in Jesus' story (v 31-33)?

**7** What is the point of each of the things that Jesus mentions about the Samaritan (v 33-35)?
What equivalent things can we do for our "neighbours" today?

---

**C  MARTHA'S QUESTION**                    Read verses 38-42

**8** Martha asks Jesus a question (v 40). What does she think is the most important thing to do (v 38-40)?

**9** As Jesus responds to Martha, what does he say is the most important thing to do (v 39-42)?

**10** We live in a pressurised world. We may have many responsibilities, including caring for others (as Jesus asks, v 29-37). How can we ensure that we share Mary's priority, rather than Martha's?

---

**D  NEXT TIME...**

...you'll be looking at Luke 11 v 1-4.

**How should I pray?**

**Today's passage: Luke 11 v 1-4**

Surveys show that a large majority of people pray, either regularly or at some stage in their lives. But most of us feel that "we're not very good at prayer" and have a lot to learn. Jesus, at the request of his disciples who saw him praying (v 1), teaches us how to pray. This prayer (v 2-4) is normally called the Lord's Prayer. It can be prayed in exactly Jesus' words (Jesus uses a fuller version in Matthew 6 v 9-13), or it can be used as a pattern for our own praying. It begins with God's concerns (prayers to advance God's purposes, v 2) and continues with our needs (v 3-4).

**A  LORD'S PRAYER: GOD'S CONCERNS Read verses 1-2**

❶ Jesus almost always calls God "Father" when praying, and taught his disciples to do the same (v 2).
What other names might we call God when we pray?
Why is it helpful, and amazing, to call God "Father" when we pray?

❷ "Hallowed be your name" means: "Let your name, and you yourself, be treated with reverence". Why should we want God the Father to be honoured?

❸ "Your kingdom come" (v 2) probably means: "May you be King in more and more areas of everyone's lives" and: "May the final day, when the whole universe bows to you as King, come soon".
Why should we want to see, and pray for, both of these things?

**B  LORD'S PRAYER: OUR NEEDS        Read verses 3-4**

❹ After such big requests in verse 2, why do you think Jesus tells us to pray: "Give us each day our daily bread" (v 3)?

**5** Why is it so necessary for God to forgive us (v 4)?
Over recent months or years, have you become more aware or less aware of your sins (ie: any area of life in which Jesus is not in control)? Why do you think that has happened?

**6** When do you find it hardest to forgive others (v 4)?
What's the connection here between God forgiving our sins and us forgiving other people (v 4)?
Does that thought help you to forgive others?

**7** What temptations do you want to pray that God will take you away from (v 4)?

---
**C  OUR PRAYER**                          **Re-read verses 1-4**
---

**8** Write down specific things you will pray for over the next few days to reflect God's concerns in verse 2.

**9** Write down specific things you will pray for over the next few days to reflect your needs in verses 3-4.

You might like to finish this session by each praying a simple prayer, either out loud or silently in your head.

---
**D  NEXT TIME...**
---

Slower Route: Luke 13 v 22-30 (p 36). Full Route: Luke 11 v 5-13 (p 30). Nothing to read before the next session! But you might decide to begin praying in a new way as a result of this passage, and talk next time about how you've got on.

# Will God answer my prayers?

## Today's passage: Luke 11 v 5-13

Jesus often taught in parables. A parable is a story (eg: v 5-8), or a set of questions (eg: v 11-12), which sheds light on the most important questions in life. Often Jesus' parables were about God. It's helpful to think of them falling into one of three categories:

1. "God is just like that". He is exactly like one of the characters in the story. One of the best-known examples is the father in the parable of "the prodigal son" (15 v 11-32).

2. "God is much better than that". A character in the story is like God, but God is much better still. Jesus often shows this by saying "how much more" (see v 13).

3. "In some ways God is like that, and in some ways he is not". A good example is 18 v 1-8. God is like the judge in the story because he "gives justice" to those who pray to him (v 7-8), and unlike the judge in the story in that he is not self-centred or uncaring.

### A   RECAP: PRAYER                    Re-read verses 1-4

❶ Has your praying been different in any way because of what you discovered in verses 1-4? If so, how?

### B   JESUS' FIRST PARABLE            Read verses 5-10

Note: Different versions translate a word in verse 8 differently: you may have "impudence", "boldness" or "persistence". The word is probably best translated "shameless persistence".

❷ What is Jesus teaching us through this parable (v 5-10)?

❸ This parable comes into the third category of parables about God. So in what ways is God *unlike* the man who is asked for bread?

**4** In what ways is God *like* the man who is asked for bread?


**JESUS' SECOND PARABLE**         **Read verses 11-13**

**5** What is Jesus teaching us through this parable (ie: these questions)?


**6** This parable comes into the second category of parables. So in what ways is God *much better than* human fathers?


**7** What does Jesus mean when he says God will "give the Holy Spirit to those who ask him" (v 13), do you think?
What does this encourage us to ask God for?


**D** **OUR PRAYER**

**8** If you pray, how will your praying be different this week because of what you've learned from this passage?


You may like to finish this session by each praying a simple prayer, either aloud or silently in your head.

**E** **NEXT TIME...**

...it's Luke 12 v 13-34.
Before next time, read up to the start of the next session's passage, and come ready to talk about anything you found interesting.

# How can Jesus help me with my money worries?

**Today's passage:** Luke 12 v 13-34

Many of us have money worries, at some stage in our life or most of the time. They can deprive us of sleep, make us work longer hours than is good for us and are a major cause of marriage breakdowns. Jesus' teaching is always realistic and down to earth, so it is no surprise that he says a great deal about money. In this passage, he encourages us to bring God in on our money concerns.

## A  RECAP: PRAYER                          Re-read 11 v 5-13

**1** Has your praying changed in any way because of what you learned from Jesus last week? If so, how?

## B  WANTING MORE                          Read 12 v 13-21

**2** Why is money so often an issue in human families (v 13)? Is it an issue in your family (only answer this if you're comfortable doing so)?

**3** What is Jesus' parable meant to teach us (v 15-21)?

**4** Saving is normally seen as a virtue. How can we think rightly about money, not "lay up treasure/store up things for ourselves" (v 15-21)?

**5** In practice, how do you think we can be "rich towards God" (v 21)?

## C  WORRIES                               Read verses 22-30

**6** What did the people who Jesus is talking to worry about (v 22-30)? What do you worry about?

**7** What reasons does Jesus give here for saying we need not worry? How could you remind yourself of these when you begin to worry?

## D TRUE SECURITY            Read verses 31-34

**8** What does Jesus tell us to set our heart on in these verses?

**9** God's "kingdom" means "God ruling as King". When Jesus says God is pleased "to give you the kingdom" (v 32), he means "to allow you to have him as your King, now and in eternity".
What will it mean for you to "seek his kingdom" in your life (v 31, 34)?

**10** What else does Jesus tell us to do (v 33)?

**11** What are the reasons Jesus gives to show his advice is wise (v 31-34)?

## E SUM UP

**12** What is the main thing you take away from this session?

If you finished the last two sessions with prayer, you could make this your regular way of finishing from now on.

## F NEXT TIME...

...you'll be looking at Luke 12 v 35-48—nothing to read before then!

**How can I be ready for Jesus?**

**Today's passage:** Luke 12 v 35-48

The answer to what one of Jesus' parables means is often in what he says immediately before or after it (or both). Here, Jesus tells two parables (v 36-39 and v 42-48). Immediately before the first parable, he says: "Be like men who are waiting for their master to come home" (v 36); immediately after it he says: "You also must be ready, for the Son of Man (ie: Jesus) is coming at an hour you do not expect" (v 40). And then he says immediately after the second parable: "Everyone to whom much was given, of him much will be required, and from him to whom they entrusted much, they will demand the more" (v48).

These are the main clues to the meaning of these parables. They are both about Jesus' promise to come back to this earth as Master and Judge at the end of time.

**A  READY FOR THE MASTER**          **Read verses 35-40**

❶ Jesus is "the master" in these verses. What is he saying about himself in this parable (v 35-40)?

❷ We are the "servants". What is Jesus saying about us here (v 35-40)?

❸ What is Jesus saying we don't know (v 39-40, see also v 46)? And what is Jesus saying that we do know about the future (v 35-40)?

❹ How do you think *we* can be ready for Jesus' return?

## B  HOW CAN I SHOW I'M READY?        Read verses 41-48

**5** Again, Jesus is "the master". What is he saying about himself in this second parable (v 42-48)?

**6** We, especially those with any responsibility for other people, are the "manager" (v 42) or "servant" (v 43). What is Jesus saying about us in this parable (v 42-48)?

**7** Peter asks Jesus who the first parable was for (v 41). Jesus doesn't answer the question directly but replies with the second parable (v42-48). Who are both parables addressed to?

Note: The clue is almost certainly in what Jesus says *immediately after* the second parable: the last part of verse 48.

**8** (a) What does the master do for the faithful servant (v 42-44)?

(b) And what does he do to the unfaithful servant (v 45-48)?

(c) What is Jesus telling us through this story about what he will do at the end of time?

## C  SUM UP

**9** What is the main thing you have learned from this session?

## D  NEXT TIME...

...you'll be studying Luke 13 v 22-30.
Before next time, read Luke 12 v 49 – 13 v 21 and come along next time ready to talk about anything you found interesting.

# Can I leave it too late?

**Today's passage: Luke 13 v 22-30**

Jesus is making his way to Jerusalem (v 22), going deliberately to the place where he knows he will be killed (see 9 v 22, 44; 18 v 31-33). Aware that he is about to die, his teaching takes on still more urgency.

He is asked a question (v 23) and, as so often, he answers with a parable (v 24-30). The "master/owner" in the story (v 25) is Jesus himself. The "house" (v 25) that we want to get into is "the kingdom of God" (v 28-29) the place where God rules as King for ever. Jesus is teaching us about our eternal future, and tells us to sort it out now, while we have the opportunity.

**A  RECAP: PRAYER** (if you're on Slower Route)  **Re-read 11 v 1-4**

❶ Has your praying changed in any way because of what you learned from Jesus last session? If so, how?

**B  THE BYSTANDER'S QUESTION**  **Read verses 22-23**

❷ Is the bystander's question an important one (v 23)? Why/why not?

**C  JESUS' ANSWER**  **Read verses 24-30**

❸ What is Jesus telling us to do (v 24)? What does that mean, do you think?

❹ Why is it important to do now, or soon, what Jesus says (v 24-25)?

❺ What are Jesus' warnings (v 24-28)?

**6** The people give reasons why they should be let in (v 25-26). Why are those reasons inadequate (v 25, 27)?

**7** What inadequate reasons for God accepting us might we put forward (like the one in v 26)?

**8** What are Jesus' positive, encouraging promises (v 29)?

**9** Jesus talks about being "in the kingdom of God" and "reclining at table/feasting/eating" (v 28-29). What is he saying our eternal future will be like, provided we "enter through the narrow door" (v 24)?

**10** What is Jesus teaching us in his last statement (v 30)? Is it a warning, or an encouraging promise, or both? Why?

**D SUM UP**

**11** What is the main thing you're taking away from this section?

If you finished the last two sessions with prayer, you could make this your regular way of finishing from now on.

**E NEXT TIME...**

Slower Route: Luke 15 v 11-24 (p 40). Full Route: Luke 14 v 15-24 (p 38). Before you next meet, read up to the start of your next session's passage, and come along ready to discuss what interested you.

# How does God react to my excuses?

## Today's passage: Luke 14 v 15-24

We've already seen this pattern: someone asks a question (13 v 23) or makes a statement (14 v 15), and Jesus responds with a parable (14 v 16-24) which gives us important teaching. In this parable:

• The master (v 21) is Jesus (or God the Father)

• The servant (v 17), sent with the master's message, is the prophets in the Bible, or Christian teachers

• The people originally invited (v 17, 24) are Jewish leaders and specifically the Pharisees (v 1)

• The poor people (v 21-23) are everybody else: ordinary Jews, and probably the whole (non-Jewish) human race

• The "great banquet/dinner" (v 16) is "the kingdom of God" (v 15)

Jesus was certainly teaching about the celebrations after the last judgment, when God will rule as King over all; he may also have been thinking of the joy of living with God as our King now.

---

### A THE INVITATIONS                    Read verses 15-17

❶ The master sent his servant to invite his guests to the banquet (v 16-17). How did Jesus' original hearers receive the invitation to come into God's kingdom? In what ways has Jesus sent *you* the invitation to come into his kingdom?

---

### B THE EXCUSES                        Read verses 18-21

❷ What are the first two excuses (v 18-19)? Why might the invited people feel they were adequate excuses?

❸ Have you ever used your working life as an excuse for not responding to Jesus' invitation to come into his kingdom?

**4** What is the third excuse? Why might the invited people feel this was an adequate excuse?

**5** Have you ever used your family life as an excuse for not responding to Jesus' invitation to come into his kingdom?

**6** How does Jesus react to these excuses (v 21)? Why?

## C THE NEW INVITATIONS          Read verses 21-24

**7** Can you see at all how you could be described as "poor, crippled, blind, lame" (v 21). If so, in what sense?

**8** Why is the master so intent on sending out yet more invitations (v 22-23)? What does this tell us about Jesus?

## D SUM UP

**9** Is the main teaching of Jesus in this parable a promise to us, or a warning to us, or both? Why?
What will you do as a result of this teaching of Jesus?

## E NEXT TIME...

...it's Luke 14 v 11-24.
Before next time, read 14 v 25 – 15 v 10, and come ready to talk about what was most on Jesus' mind during this section of his teaching.

**How can I come back to God?**

**Today's passage:** Luke 15 v 11-24

This is probably Jesus' most famous parable. The father in the story (v 12) is God. The younger son (v 12) is us. Wanting our "share of the property/ estate" (v 12) is wanting to live our life with no interference from God.

The story is normally known as "The Prodigal Son". But it could just as well be called "The Forgiving Father". It is as much about the father as the son, as much about God as about us.

We'll try to keep both in mind and see what Jesus is teaching about how we can come back to God.

**A  LEAVING HOME**                          **Read verses 11-13**

❶ What does the son want (v 12-13)?
  What is Jesus telling us in v 12-13 about our attitude to God?

❷ What does the father allow (v 12-13)?
  What is Jesus telling us in v 12-13 about God's attitude to us?

**B  FINDING IT TOUGH**                       **Read verses 14-16**

❸ How does life in fact turn out for the son (v 14-16)?

❹ What is Jesus telling us in v 14-16 about a life lived apart from God?
  Is that in any way true of your present, or past, experience?

**C  FACING THE TRUTH**                        **Read verses 17-19**

❺ What is the turning point for the son (v 17)?

**6** What does he feel he can do (v 18-19)?

**7** What is Jesus saying that it's necessary to realise before we can come back to God (v 17-19)?
Have you come to realise this more over recent months?

**D** COMING HOME                              Read verses 20-24

**8** What does the son actually do (v 20-21)?

**9** What is Jesus telling us in verses 20-21 that we must do?
How can we do it in practice?

**10** What does the father do (v 20-24)?
What is Jesus telling us in v 20-24 about God's attitude to us?

**11** How does God view us after we have come back to him (v 24)?
Why does verse 24 use such strong language, do you think?

**E** SUM UP

**12** What is the main message you're taking away from Jesus' teaching?

**F** NEXT TIME...

Quick and Slower Routes: 23 v 32-49 (p 48). Full route: 18 v 9-14 (p 42).
As you read up to the start of the next session's passage, note down anything that you find particularly interesting or surprising.

**What kind of person does God accept?**

**Today's passage:** Luke 18 v 9-14

Jesus is most concerned with people's attitudes, especially our attitude towards God. Of course he cares about what we do publicly (eg: v 12) and in what we say. But he is more interested in the inner attitude of our heart. This, he says, will show whether God will accept us.

As so often, he underlines this truth by using a parable about two contrasting men: a Pharisee (a Jewish religious leader) and a tax collector (someone who worked for the hated Roman or Herodian authorities).

## A  THE PHARISEE                                    Read verses 9-12

❶ What is true in what the Pharisee says (v 10-12)?

❷ What is wrong about what the Pharisee feels (v 9-12, 14)? Why is it wrong?

❸ When, if you're honest, do you find yourself feeling like the Pharisee (if ever)?

## B  THE TAX COLLECTOR                              Read verse 13

❹ What is true in what the tax collector says (v 13)?

❺ What is right about what the tax collector feels (v 13-14)? Why is it right?

**6** When, if you're honest, do you find yourself feeling like the tax collector (if ever)?

## C GOD'S VERDICT                     Read verse 14

**7** "Justified" means "being put in the right with God" or "declared guilt-free". Why does God come to this unexpected verdict (v 14)?

## D STANDING BACK                    Re-read verses 9-14

**8** What is the main truth that Jesus wants us to take away from this story of his (v 9-14)?

**9** In practice, how can we genuinely humble ourselves before God (v 13-14)?

**10** What does it mean when Jesus says that God will exalt us if we do humble ourselves (v 14)?

## E SUM UP

**11** Is there anything you need to do/change as a result of discussing this teaching of Jesus (v 9-14)?

This is a passage not only about our attitudes, but also about our praying (v 10). Would you like to finish by praying aloud together?

## F NEXT TIME...

...you'll be looking at Luke 22 v 14-20.
   Before next time, read Luke 18 v 15 – 22 v 13.

# What does the communion service mean?

**Today's passage: Luke 22 v 14-20**

Jesus loved the Old Testament, and lived by it (for example 4 v 4, 8, 12). He taught that it was God's word, and should be obeyed.

So, of course, he celebrated the Passover (v 15). This was the annual meal in which Jews celebrated how God had spared ("passed over") the Jews when all the firstborn of Egypt were destroyed, and how he had then saved the Jews from the Egyptian army that was pursuing them (you can read the full story in Exodus 12 v 1-32 and 14 v 5-31). This Passover meal involved drinking several cups of wine (v 17, 20) and eating special bread (v 19).

Now, at his last Passover, Jesus gives new and deeper meaning to the meal, and makes the bread and the wine pictures, or symbols, of what he is about to do.

The meal is normally called the Last Supper; it is also the first communion service.

---

**A WHAT JESUS FORETOLD**　　　　　**Read verses 14-18**

❶ What does Jesus say lies ahead for him (v 14-18)?

❷ Jesus predicts that he will eat the Passover again when "it is fulfilled in the kingdom of God" (v 16), and that he will drink wine again when "the kingdom of God comes" (v 18). What time is he referring to?

Note: It may help you to re-read where Jesus has already spoken about a future meal, or banquet—have a look at 13 v 28-29 and 14 v 15-24.

❸ What do Jesus' words here tell us about the future celebrations when God will be honoured as King (v 16-18)?

**4** What does Jesus make the broken bread a picture, or symbol, of (v 19)?

**5** In what sense has Christ's body been "given for" us, do you think (v 19)?

**6** In what way can we best remember Jesus and his death for us (v 19)?

**7** What does Jesus make the cup of wine a picture of (v 20)?

**8** A "covenant" is an agreement made between two people, establishing a new relationship between them (for example, a wedding brings into being a marriage covenant). What is "the new covenant" (v 20) which Jesus' blood (ie: his death) brings into being?

**C** SUM UP

**9** What is Jesus saying, with the broken bread and poured out wine, about *why* he is going to die (v 15-20)?

**10** What is the main thing you have learned from this session?

**D** NEXT TIME...

Luke 22 v 31-34 and 54-62.
     Before next time, read Luke 22 v 21-30 and come ready to talk about Jesus' view of true greatness.

# What happens when I let Jesus down?

**Today's passage: Luke 22 v 31-34 and 54-62**

Only one man in the Bible, and the whole of history, is sinless. The other Bible "heroes" are always shown to us warts and all. That is certainly the case with Jesus' disciple, Simon, who was normally known by his nickname, Peter (and who we've met in Sessions 5, 9 and 14).

The Bible shows us these faults to enable us to be honest about our own sins, and to encourage us that Jesus can still forgive us, reaffirm his love for us and use us in his service. They show us that you don't have to be perfect to become, or to stay, a Christian; an imperfect person can acknowledge their sin and come, or come back, to Jesus.

---

**A NOT LISTENING TO THE WARNING Read verses 31-34**

**1** Jesus speaks about Satan (v 31). Is Jesus teaching us the devil is real? If so, what does Satan want to do (v 31-32)?

**2** What help does Jesus offer when Simon Peter is attacked by Satan (v 32)? Jesus seems to think that help is important. Why?

**3** What is Peter to do after he has let Jesus down (v 32)? Why is that important?

**4** In what ways is Peter over-confident (v 33-34)? Are we sometimes over-confident that we will not let Jesus down?

---

**B LETTING JESUS DOWN**          **Read verses 54-62**

**5** Why do you think Peter let Jesus down with very ordinary (ie: not powerful) people (v 54-60)?

**6** Do we sometimes let Jesus down in very ordinary situations? If so, when?




**7** What happens when Peter lets Jesus down (v 61-62)?



**8** Does it upset us when we let Jesus down? Why/why not?




**C** **RECAP** **Re-read verses 31-32**

**9** Verse 62 is not the end of the story. What happens after Peter lets Jesus down (v 32)?



**10** What is verse 32 telling us to do when we have disappointed Jesus?




**D** **SUM UP**

**11** What is the main thing you are taking away from this story of Jesus and Peter?




**E** **NEXT TIME...**

...you'll be studying Luke 24 v 32-49.
 Before next time, read Luke 22 v 39-53, 63-71 and 23 v 1-31, and come ready to talk about what most strikes you about what Jesus went through for us.

# How do I respond to Jesus' death?

**Today's passage: Luke 23 v 32-47**

The death of Jesus has always divided people. It is the central event in Christianity and (many would say) in human history. Some people are drawn to the dying love of Jesus, which opens the way to forgiveness and paradise (v 43); others are repelled by what they see as weakness.

Luke, in his account of Christ's death, introduces us to a whole range of individuals and groups, who all react to Jesus in different ways. These verses make us ask: How do *I* respond to Jesus' death on the cross?

## A JESUS AND THE MOCKERS          Read verses 32-38

❶ How does Jesus respond to the way he is being treated (v 32-34)? What does this tell us about Jesus?

❷ How do the crowd (people, rulers/leaders, soldiers) react to Jesus (v 35-38)?
Do you see the same attitudes in people today? If so, in what ways?

## B THE TWO CRIMINALS          Read verses 39-43

❸ How does the first criminal react to Jesus (v 39)?

❹ How does the second criminal react to the situation (v 40-42)? What does he realise that makes him react so differently (v 40-42)?

❺ What is Jesus' promise to the second criminal (v 43)?
What does all this tell us about what kind of people will be with Jesus after their death (v 39-43)?

## C  JESUS AND GOD THE FATHER        Read verses 44-46

**6** God the Father isn't mentioned in v 44-45, but it's obvious that Luke thinks he's behind these events. Why do you think God brings darkness to the land from 12 noon to 3pm (v 44-45). *If you're stuck, have a look at what God said in the Old Testament book of Amos, chapter 8 v 9-14, where he is talking about what he will do in the future.*

**7** The "curtain of the temple" separated off the most holy inner part of the Jerusalem Temple, where God's presence was especially present (see, for example, Exodus 26 v 33). Ordinary Jews were not allowed past, or even near, this curtain: it was like a huge "no entry" sign between God and humans. Luke clearly thinks the tearing of this curtain was very significant. What do you think it means (v 45)?

**8** What is Jesus' attitude as he dies (v 46)?
What does this tell us about him?

## D  THE SOLDIER                      Read verse 47

**9** What conclusion does the centurion come to (v 47)?
What do you think makes him believe this (v 32-47)?

## E  AND THEN THERE'S US              Read verses 32-47

**10** What are your feelings about / reactions to the death of Jesus (v 32-49)? Why do you feel that way?

## F  NEXT TIME...

Quick and Slower Routes: 24 v 13-35 (p 56). Full Route: 24 v 1-12 (p 54).
If you're not doing Session 22, answer the questions on the next four pages. Also, fill in the "What Next?" section on page 60. If you are doing Session 22, do the next four pages *after* that session.

49

# Where you're at now

In your first session together, you talked about the different stages you had been through in your thinking about Jesus. If these studies have been helpful, they will have moved you on in your thinking.

The material on the next three pages sets out, as clearly as possible, the central message of Jesus (using only passages from the Quick Route version of this booklet), and explains what it means to be a committed Christian. If you were not a committed Christian when you began these studies (and perhaps still are not), please answer question (a) in each section. If you were a committed Christian when you began these studies, answer question (b).

## THE ABCD OF JESUS' MESSAGE

To become a committed Christian means that you are able to:

**A**DMIT: I AM NOT WORTHY TO BE GOD'S CHILD (15 v 19, 21). Like the "prodigal son", we need to "come to our senses" and acknowledge that we've "squandered" much of our life by living it away from God, our perfect Father. We have sinned and are not worthy of a relationship with God (15 v 11-19).

(a) Can you admit that in God's eyes you are not a good person, but instead a person who is unworthy of him, needing his forgiveness? If so, will you tell him so? If not, why do you find this difficult?

(b) As you go on in your life as a Christian, do you become more or less aware of your own sinfulness?
Is this an encouraging or discouraging sign? Why?

**B**ELIEVE: JESUS SAVED ME BY DYING IN MY PLACE (23 v 35-39).
Right from his birth, Jesus was introduced as our Saviour (2 v 11), the
one who'd come to rescue us. He did this by dying on the cross. There is
deliberate irony in the way people said to him as he died: "Save yourself
and us!" (23 v 39). That is precisely what he could not do: it was one or
the other. He could either save himself from death—and then no human
would be saved. Or he could die on the cross, taking our sin and guilt on
himself, and then everyone who responds to him can be saved—rescued
and forgiven (23 v 40-43).

(a) Can you believe and accept that Jesus died in your place, taking your
     sins on himself?
     If so, will you thank him for this? If not, why do you find this difficult?

(b) As you go on in your life as a Christian, is the death of Jesus
     becoming more, or less, central to your thinking?
     Is this an encouraging or discouraging sign?  Why?

**C**ONSIDER: JESUS IS GOING TO BE MY LORD (2 v 11).
The angels announced that Jesus would not only be Saviour but also
Lord (2 v 11). A Christian is someone who listens carefully to Jesus'
teaching, takes it to heart (rather than ignoring or arguing with it) and
seeks increasingly to obey it, even though they will still fail. There is a
cost to becoming a Christian, but the cost of not responding to Christ is
greater (13 v 27-28).

(a) Have you considered the cost of becoming a Christian (and the cost
     of not doing so)? Are you wanting to make Jesus your Lord?
     If so, will you tell him so? If not, why do you find this difficult?

(b) As you go on in your life as a Christian, are there more and more areas of your life over which Christ is Lord?
If so, will you thank him for this? If not, is there some specific area you need to hand over to him as Lord?


**D**O: I MUST ASK JESUS FOR HIS NEW LIFE (23 v 42.)

The "prodigal son" came to his father and asked for his forgiveness (15 v 20-21); the criminal being crucified turned to Jesus and asked for a new beginning (23 v 42-43). When we do this, our new life—as a son or daughter of God—begins. God says of us: "This my son (or daughter), who was dead and is alive again; (s)he was lost and is found" (15 v 24).

(a) Are you now ready to come to Christ and give your life to him, so that you can receive new, and eternal, life from him?
If so, we suggest that you use the prayer towards the end of this page. If not, what is it that is stopping you from doing so?


(b) As you go on in your life as a Christian, are you more aware, or less aware, of the change in you that God brought about when you came to Christ?
Is this an encouraging or discouraging sign?  Why?

## A PRAYER OF COMMITMENT

Lord Jesus Christ, I admit that I have lived much of my life apart from God and that I am not worthy to be his child. I am ashamed of this.
I believe that you died on the cross in my place, taking my sins and guilt onto yourself. I am so grateful for that.
I have considered what it means to make you my Lord, to listen to your teaching and to seek to obey you. I want you to be my Lord.
Right now, I come to you and ask for your new life. Thank you that from now on I am truly your child, forgiven and loved.
Thank you. Amen.

## AT YOUR NEXT SESSION

Take the first 10-15 minutes to talk together about your answers to these questions.

# What happened on Easter Sunday?

**Today's passage: Luke 24 v 1-12**

One of the best ways to understand the events described in the Gospels (or in other parts of the Bible) is to imagine you were there. At the beginning of the first Easter Day the women (v 10) and Peter (v 12) had no idea what was about to happen. Try to put yourself in their shoes. It is a good way to find the answer to the question: What exactly did happen on the first Easter Day?

## A WHAT THE WOMEN FOUND          Read verses 1-3

❶ The stone sealed off the mouth of the rock-cut tomb. Why are the women (v 10) "perplexed"/"wondering" when they find the stone rolled away and the body gone (v 1-3)?
What explanations might be going through their mind at this point?

## B WHAT THEY SAW AND HEARD          Read verses 4-8

❷ How do the women react to the two men (v 4-5)? Why?

❸ What do the two men tell them (v 5-7)?

❹ Why should what they've seen not be surprising to them (v 6-7)?

❺ Why do you think they hadn't remembered Jesus' words before?

## C  WHAT THEY SAID                      Read verses 9-11

**6** What do the women tell the apostles (v 9-10)?
How do the apostles respond (v 11)? Why?

**7** Do you ever find yourself reacting as the apostles did to what the
Bible says happened on the first Easter Sunday (v 11)? Why/why not?

## D  WHAT PETER FOUND                    Read verse 12

**8** Why do you think Peter runs to the tomb (v 12)?

**9** Why does he walk home "marvelling"/wondering"/"amazed at" what
he finds at the tomb (v 12)?

## E  SUM UP

**10** What has most caused you to think that the Easter story is, or might
be, true?

## F  NEXT TIME...

...it's Luke 24 v 13-35.
Before next time, please fill in your answers to the questions which
begin on page 50. Come along ready to talk through them for the first
ten minutes or so of your next session.

# What's the evidence that Jesus is alive?

## A WHERE YOU'RE AT NOW

Take 10 to 15 minutes (or as long as you need) to talk together about your answers to the questions on page 50-52. If there's enough to talk about to fill your whole time this week, that's fine! You can come back to Luke 24 v 13-35 in your next session together.

If this discussion raises issues about which neither of you knows the answer, why not invite the pastor of your local church, or a more mature Christian who one or both of you know, to meet up with you and talk about the questions you have?

**Today's passage: Luke 24 v 13-35**

It's often claimed that there's no hard evidence for the Christian faith, and that to become a committed Christian is just a blind leap of faith. The Bible takes an exactly opposite viewpoint: there is a great deal of evidence for the truth of Christianity, and the "blind" people are those who can't see that Jesus is alive today (see v 16, 31). This session looks at just some of that evidence.

## B HOPES DASHED                    Read verses 13-21

❶ What have the two walkers come to believe about Jesus, and why are they disappointed now (v 13-21)?

❷ Why would the Christian faith be a disappointment to us now if Jesus *wasn't* alive today?

## C EVIDENCE IGNORED                 Read verses 22-24

❸ What evidence do they have already that Jesus is alive (v 21-24)? So why are they still disappointed, do you think?

**4** Is there any evidence you have, but tend to overlook or underestimate, that Jesus is alive and active today?

## D EVIDENCE SUPPLIED                     Read verses 25-27

**5** What evidence does Jesus put before them (v 25-27)?

**6** In what ways (if any) has reading the Gospel of Luke helped you to believe in Jesus?

## E EVIDENCE OF EXPERIENCE              Read verses 27-35

**7** What experiences do this pair have which convince them that Jesus is alive (v 27-35)?

**8** Have you had any experiences which have encouraged you to believe that Jesus is alive? What were they?

## F SUM UP

**9** What is the main thing that you will take away from this session?

## G NEXT TIME...

If this is your last session, discuss the "What Next?" section on page 60, which hopefully you've already filled in (if not, you can do it now!)
Full Route next time: Luke 24 v 36-49 (p 58). Nothing to read before then, but fill in the "What Next?" section on page 60.

# What am I to do now?

**Today's passage:** Luke 24 v 36-53

Luke finishes his Gospel with the risen Christ appearing to his eleven closest disciples, and giving them instructions about what to do from now on. He ends as Jesus goes back to heaven (v 50-53).

As so often, the best way to approach this passage is to put yourself in the disciples' shoes, and to imagine these events happening to you.

## A THE SURPRISE                    Read verses 36-43

❶ The disciples have already heard that Jesus has risen from the dead and appeared to others (v 33-35). So why, when the risen Jesus comes to them, do they react in the way v 37-38 describes?

❷ In what different ways does Jesus convince the disciples that he really has risen from the dead (v 36-43)?

❸ Some people say: "It's not important whether or not Jesus' body was raised from the dead; what's important is that Jesus' influence lives on". Based on verses 36-43, what do you make of that idea?

❹ What effect would it have if you realised Jesus is alive today and gave your life to him (or, if you are already a Christian, what effect has it had)?

## B  THE UNDERSTANDING                    Read verses 44-47

**5** What does Jesus teach about the relationship between the Old Testament and himself (v 44-47)?

**6** People today often dismiss the Old Testament as out of date, or dull. How does Jesus say that a Christian should approach the Old Testament (v 44-47)?


## C  THE MISSION                          Read verses 46-53

**7** Jesus has now risen from the dead. What is to happen next (v 46-48)?


**8** What is the heart of the Christian message (v 46-47)?
In what ways has your thinking about the heart of the Christian message changed as you've read Luke's Gospel?


**9** "The promise" (v 49) is the Holy Spirit, who God sent a few days later at the Pentecost festival (see Acts 1 v 4-5, 2 v 1-41). Why would the way Jesus is described in verse 50 be very reassuring to his followers?


## D  SUM UP

**10** What is the main thing that has struck you from this session?


## E  WHAT NEXT?

Discuss the "What Next?" section you've (hopefully!) already filled in.

You are coming to the end of *One2One Just Looking*. This page is here to help you review your sessions together, and decide where to go from here. Please fill in your response to the questions and come to your final session ready to discuss what you have written.

1.  What have you enjoyed most about your sessions together?

2.  What (if anything) would you suggest doing differently if you continued in the same Bible-reading partnership or started a new Bible-reading partnership with someone else?

3.  Now that you have finished studying Luke's Gospel together, do you want:
    *   to continue meeting together and discussing the Bible?
        *A natural next step would be to order One2One Book One, published by The Good Book Company.*
    *   to join a "small group" (probably between eight and twelve people meeting midweek) to study the Bible?
    *   to read a book about the Christian faith?
    *   to join a course investigating Christianity, such as *Christianity Explored* (visit www.christianityexplored.org/course)?
    *   to do nothing more at this stage?

## STILL LOOKING?

There is definitely a time to be "Just Looking"; it would be foolish to commit to following Jesus without taking time to think. But some people go on "Just Looking" for ever, and never come to a conclusion. One of God's Old Testament messengers, Elijah, challenged people in his day: "How long will you go on limping between two opinions?" (1 Kings 18 v 21). Ultimately, we all have to make our choice.

Is it time for you to go back to the "Where you're at now" section of this book (pages 50-53) and come to a clear decision?

If there is someone in charge of a church's Bible-reading partnerships who you got this book from, please make a photocopy of the previous page and (if you are happy to do this) send or give the copy to him/her.

# Keep on looking...
## www.christianityexplored.org

The Christianity Explored website enables you to keep exploring Jesus' life and message in your own way, at your own pace. It features:

- answers to tough questions
- a visual outline explaining what Christianity is
- real life stories of people's experiences of becoming Christians.

Hundreds of thousands have found it helps them think through what they believe: we hope you find the same!

# Dig deeper...
# keep on reading the Bible

## Explore

Many Christians love to regularly read the Bible
and pray—but it can be hard to get going with
that! That's where *Explore* can help. Each issue
features three months of daily readings to help you
understand and apply the message and challenge of
God's word.

Our introductory edition of *Explore* is called *Time
with God*. It contains 28 studies and it's designed to
help Christians develop the discipline of a regular
quiet time.

## Table Talk

Many parents struggle to read the Bible consistently
with their children—but help is at hand. *Table Talk*
is designed to form the basis for a short family Bible
time—maybe just five minutes at breakfast or dinner.
It includes a simple discussion starter or activity that
leads into a short Bible reading and some ideas for
prayer.

## Good Book Guides

*Good Book Guides* seek to uncover the meaning of a
passage and see how it fits into the big picture of the
Bible while leading people to apply what they have
learned to their lives. *Good Book Guides* are ideal for
small groups or individual study.

UK & Europe: www.thegoodbook.co.uk
N America: www.thegoodbook.com
Australia: www.thegoodbook.com.au
New Zealand: www.thegoodbook.co.nz

# thegoodbook
## COMPANY

At The Good Book Company, we are dedicated to helping Christians and local churches grow. We believe that God's growth process always starts with hearing clearly what he has said to us through his timeless word—the Bible.

Ever since we opened our doors in 1991, we have been striving to produce resources that honour God in the way the Bible is used. We have grown to become an international provider of user-friendly resources to the Christian community, with believers of all backgrounds and denominations using our Bible studies, books, resources for those wanting to find out about the Christian faith, DVD-based courses and training events.

We want to equip ordinary Christians to live for Christ day by day, help churches to grow in their knowledge of God and their love for one another, and enable people to explore the Christian message and think it through for themselves. Call us for a discussion of your needs, or visit one of our websites for more information on the resources and services we provide, and how to obtain our materials throughout the world.

**UK & Europe:** www.thegoodbook.co.uk
**N America:** www.thegoodbook.com
**Australia:** www.thegoodbook.com.au
**New Zealand:** www.thegoodbook.co.nz

**Tel UK:** 0345 225 0880
**Tel International:** +44 (0) 208 942 0880

---

## Also available in the One2One series...
### One2One Book One

Don't miss Andrew Cornes' first One2One study guide featuring:

- 24 studies on John, Philippians and Psalms for Bible-reading partnerships

- Review sheets to help evaluate your time with your Bible-reading partner

one2one                    1

John | Philippians | Psalms
24 studies for Bible Reading Partnerships

Andrew Cornes